# Breaking Free
## from the
## Victim Mentality

# Breaking Free
## from the
# Victim Mentality

A Study Guide/Personal Journal for

## Me Man, You Woman
Jane's Deliverance from an Abusive Marriage

## Rhonda Tarver and Trudy Michalak

Rhonda Tarver 832-731-6563
www.ourdestinypublishing.com

Trudy Michalak
832-654-7177
www.janeshouseministries.org

MISSOURI CITY, TEXAS

First printing 2008

ISBN 9780979191114
LCCN 2007930492

**ATTENTION CORPORATIONS, UNIVERSITIES, COLLEGES, AND PROFESSIONAL ORGANIZATIONS:** Quantity discounts are available on bulk purchases of this book for educational, gift purposes, or as premiums for increasing magazine subscriptions or renewals. Special books or book excerpts can also be created to fit specific needs. For information, please contact Our Destiny Publishing, LLC, 5680 Highway 6 South #390, Missouri City, TX 77459; (281) 933-4990 or (866) 933-4990; www.ourdestinypublishing.com.

# Table of Contents

# Introduction

*The goal of this* study guide is to teach women to break free from a victim mentality that not only attracts abusive men, but keeps women bound in abusive relationships. This guide is not a broad-stroke attempt to stamp out domestic violence—that is an elephant entirely too big to eat in one bite.

We may not see ourselves as those who would fall for abusive men or remain in abusive relationships. But we don't always see ourselves as others do; we have blind spots. This is why it is so important that young girls and women realize and appreciate their self-worth.

The term "self-worth" can be somewhat misleading. Our sense of worth does not come from "self" but from realizing our value to the One who created us. On our own, we cannot become the amazing people of incredible destiny we were created to be. It is only through God that we can truly realize our worth and fully enter into the wildly exciting life He planned for each of us before we were ever born.

This study guide is based on the true story of "Jane's" escape from a five-year nightmare in which she was verbally, emotionally, and physically abused by her husband. Her life with an abusive partner is chronicled in the companion book, *Me Man, You Woman: Jane's Deliverance from an Abusive Marriage*. While writing the book, both Jane and I had our eyes opened to various character traits and behaviors common to women who seem to attract abusive men.

1

As we processed the material in this book, we discovered that it's easy to spot abusive men. What is much more difficult is taking responsibility for the only thing we are accountable for: ourselves. Blaming the abuser is not a viable solution to the problem of abusive relationships. Granted, it is easier to blame the abuser, but that will only solve the problem until the next abuser comes along.

Teaching women to value themselves and to trust God with their relationships—and every other area of their lives—is the only place where the solution can truly begin. This study guide contains life-changing—and even life-saving—insight that every young girl and woman needs to know.

One thing is certain: No one enters a relationship if they know beforehand that their partner may be possessive, controlling, violent, or abusive. No one knows the future—and no person or book can tell us how any of our relationships will turn out. There are, however, indicators of abusive personality types that can warn us. We are not responsible for the future, but we are responsible for recognizing and taking seriously the warning signs early in our relationships before it is too late.

Listed below are character traits typically associated with abusive personalities (www.aardvarc.org). If you are involved in a relationship you suspect might lead to abuse, please make a thoughtful, honest inventory of your partner's character. In your journal, check each characteristic that describes your partner.

- Has low self-esteem
- Rushes into relationships
- Is excessively jealous
- Is controlling
- Has unrealistic expectations or demands
- Uses isolation to keep you centered on him
- Believes in male supremacy and the stereotyped masculine role in the family

- Uses force during sex
- Has poor communication skills
- Uses negative behaviors (drugs, alcohol, battering) to cope with stress
- Blames others for his actions
- Is prone to hypersensitivity
- Presents dual or multiple personalities
- Is cruel to animals or children

Jane's story is intended to encourage women who are currently in or recovering from abusive relationships of any kind. It is proof that, once a woman has made up her mind to break free and to trust God, there is definitely hope for her future. In fact, He is our only real hope.

In Jane's case, as in all other cases like hers, the five-year nightmare of abuse could have been eliminated altogether. It simply did not have to happen.

Jane would have never agreed with that statement when we first began to write her book. She steadfastly maintained that she had been a victim and that her life had been stolen from her. If she had remained blind to her involvement in the abusive partnership, there would have been no point in sharing her story. It would not have helped anyone, not even Jane. Maybe she would have felt a little lighter for having aired her dirty laundry, but no permanent changes could have taken place until she owned up to her part.

If Jane had refused to relinquish her status as a victim, she most certainly would have moved into another destructive, possibly life-threatening relationship, given the "right" set of circumstances. Instead, she took a brutally honest personal inventory and learned what led her into the predicament in the first place.

Many women in her situation won't go that route. It is not, after all, the easiest way to go. It is much less demanding to blame an abusive partner. After all, abused women do have the sympathies of public opinion. And so they remain convinced that life happens to them, that relationships are in charge of them, and that they are helpless, hopeless, and, ultimately, not responsible.

Thanks to Jane's willingness to be completely honest and remarkably transparent, we can learn from her painful past and benefit from her eye-opening journey toward becoming a responsible adult—no longer a victim.

If you are reading this on your own, you will have ample opportunity to do your own soul searching. Discussion groups and abuse-recovery classes can benefit from the support of and interaction between women who have "been there" and understand.

To benefit fully from this study guide, I suggest you round up your Bible, your journal, a couple of pens, and several different colored highlighters—and especially your willingness to have your blind spots exposed. You will need all of these beginning with Section I.

# The Generational Cycle

———◆———

*Jane's first marriage began* with a storybook romance and wedding. She lived in bliss with the man of her dreams for over fifteen years. She had a beautiful family and a warm, stable home. Even after the untimely death of her beloved husband, Jane's children adored her, she had a host of dedicated friends, a supportive church family, plenty of money available for a fresh start, and, most important, a close relationship with the Lord her God. Jane had resources and relationships that some women don't ever have or experience.

In spite of all her "advantages," Jane still wound up in an abusive relationship, which continued as an abusive marriage. She knew that the man with whom she was sharing her life was potentially dangerous. Or did she? There were plenty of signs along the way, and a slew of friends, business associates, and even mere acquaintances said out loud what Jane refused to acknowledge. How, then, did an intelligent, attractive woman end up in the control of an abusive partner?

Jane's background reveals a generational cycle: a pattern of behavior that is passed down from parents to children, grandchildren, and on to many successive generations. Generational cycles don't just fade away with time. Left unbroken, a multigenerational pattern continues in full force and effect until someone directly addresses it and consciously breaks it. In this case, that someone was Jane. Through her relationship with Jesus Christ, trusted spiritual leaders, and friends, generational cycles were addressed and broken.

## Identifying the Cycle

The first step in breaking free of abuser/victim relational patterns is to recognize them for what they are.

Jane's mother had been born with a physical handicap, which made her a target for her own alcohol-fueled, abusive father to assault her verbally and physically. In essence, Jane's mother was a child slave, forced to work like an adult at a tender age and to forfeit her education to take care of her sick mother. Her family lacked the money for essentials such as food, clothing, and electricity but somehow managed to keep an ongoing supply of liquor.

Not only did Jane's mother lack a formal education, she had no social skills. Her primary goal in life was to survive. She didn't have the time or the opportunity to dream about her future or to make the kinds of plans young girls typically make. Her greatest dream was to escape from her nightmarish life, and the only way to accomplish that, she figured, was by way of a man. Surely, one day a man would mysteriously appear to whisk her away and take care of her the rest of her life.

Jane's own mother did not have the sense of self-worth usually found in young women who set goals, believe in themselves, and carefully evaluate whether suitors have the qualities they want in a potential mate.

As a result, Jane's mother was an abused woman who completely lacked resources. She had no friends, church family, or anyone else to encourage her and tell her she had a heavenly Father who loved and cared for her. Her impression of God, like that of most children who have hostile, abusive fathers, was not one of loving kindness. She had no reason to believe He wanted or had the ability to help her. Jane's mother knew of no examples of healthy, godly marriages, and had no reason to believe there was hope for her.

She proved herself right when she took matters into her own hands and became involved with a man she hoped would rescue her. Instead, she ended up living with that man in the same shack with the rest of her family. Sadly, he turned out to be an abusive drunk, just like her father. Pregnant before they eventually married, Jane's mother bore two children with the man, while continuing to live in the same house with the father from whom she had tried to escape.

Even more humiliating to Jane's mother was the fact that her abusive husband abandoned her, leaving her with two children and no way to support them. She fled to another state, where she lived with another family member and survived financially by way of government assistance.

By the time her knight in shining armor appeared, Jane's mother was worn out and full of despair. She was only too happy to allow her rescuer (Jane's father) to take charge of her life. For the first time ever, someone truly loved her and wanted only the best for her. He didn't care that she had two children by another man or that she was uneducated and had no social graces.

Although her parents produced two more children out of wedlock before marrying and giving birth to their third and last child, Jane's father never strayed from her mother or the family. He was decent, honest, and hardworking. A God-fearing man, he exhibited the kind of unconditional love that so many Christian marriages are missing today. He was a wonderful provider, a kind and constant encourager, and a devoted caretaker. Who could blame Jane's mother for wanting to kick back and let him serve her?

Having never been nurtured herself, Jane's mother lacked the emotional depth to nurture Jane. Her father, on the other hand, was kind and gentle, and assured Jane that he and her mother loved her deeply. Still, it was twenty-five years before Jane's mother would say the words Jane had never heard: "I love you."

Not knowing her mother's dismal background made it all the more frustrating for Jane when she was forced to clean house for days at a time while her mother sat back, watched soap operas, and "supervised." She didn't understand why her father worked so hard, then came home and helped cook, do laundry, and take care of the kids while her mother seemed to be immobilized, both emotionally and physically.

Jane suspected that her father made plenty of money, but for some reason, their belongings were frequently repossessed. Knowing that her mother was in charge of the finances, rather than her responsible and trustworthy father, Jane lived in constant fear that she would go without food and other necessities of life.

Unlike other mothers, Jane's did not teach her how to cook, dress, manage money, or take care of herself. Jane's mother never encouraged her in her school activities or homework, nor did she support Jane's goals or dreams. In fact, Jane's mother never asked her if she had goals or dreams.

Jane was saddled with a burden of guilt at an early age. One Christmas, when the family could not afford a Christmas tree, Jane's mother blatantly stated that it was Jane's fault: that she had been a bad girl. Rather than explain that daddy's job was not going well or that she had squandered all the money, Jane's mother projected her own guilt onto a deeply hurt little girl. Furthermore, it wasn't uncommon for Jane's birthday to be forgotten altogether or for her to receive fewer Christmas gifts than anyone else in the family. On one such occasion, she was the only one to receive no Christmas gifts at all, which cemented the rejection to which she had grown accustomed.

Jane's assessment of her mother at the time was that she was selfish, lazy, angry, and uncaring. Because of the deep wounds received from her mother, Jane developed judgments, bitterness, and unforgiveness toward her. Unforgiveness is the mechanism that causes the very thing we judge to be passed on to us. As a result, Jane herself grew increasingly selfish, lazy, angry, and uncaring. On the other hand, Jane was absolutely blind to any faults her father may have had. She developed an inflated image of him and subsequently developed an elaborate daydream of being rescued by a man just like her dad.

## Repeating the Cycle

Although she had had early aspirations of becoming an attorney, a detective, a doctor, or a nurse, Jane's dreams could not be sustained in an environment that was shut down with bitterness. And besides, Jane's mother had no regard for education and no experience with dreaming. Instead of pursuing a life of accomplishment and adventure, Jane adopted her mother's attitude in at least a couple of areas. She had no use for school, and she had no goals to fulfill. She set her hope completely on having a man rescue her, just like her mother.

Because of Jane's judgments against her mother, she began to follow in her footsteps without realizing it. When she met Daniel, Jane set her sights on marrying him and living a carefree life of watching soap operas and taking it easy. Unswervingly focused on her goal, Jane endured years of heartache and emotional torment under her mother's roof before Daniel appeared as the rescuing hero—just as her own father had. That was a huge gamble on her part, and no less than a miracle that it happened the way it did.

In the meantime, Jane had adopted her mother's laziness and appetite for soap operas. Uncultured by her mother, she had nothing to offer in the way of being a homemaker or a wife. She had accomplished her goal of getting married; now it was time to kick back and let her husband take care of her. The problem was, Daniel didn't share Jane's view of an "ideal" marriage. He wanted neither the power nor the responsibility to control her life.

## Making the Connection

Early in Jane's childhood, she adopted her mother's view of education: It wasn't important. She also assumed her mother's attitude toward money: There was never going to be enough, so you might as well spend the money you have on things that will make you feel better. If you have to do without something, you might as well look and feel good in the meantime.

Jane also had no training in social graces, which left her feeling inadequate and unworthy around other people. The way she chose to fit in with others was to party. She loved to dance, drink, stay up all night, and sleep during the day.

Although Jane accepted Jesus Christ as her Savior when she was eleven years old, she had no mentors or teachers from her church and no real support from spiritually-mature adults. Jane's father modeled the Heavenly Father's nature to Jane. Her mother did not have such an advantage. Jane's mother's father was morally broken and emotionally distant. Because of this, Jane grew up with a much healthier view of God than her mother did. She simply was not aware that she could have an intimate relationship with Him or that He had a plan for her life.

With no education and no intimacy with God, Jane had no motivation to establish goals or pursue her dreams. In fact, Jane's original dreams of becoming an attorney or a detective were met with little enthusiasm by her mother, who had a defeatist attitude and no regard for achievement. Jane's desire to become a doctor or a nurse was likewise undermined. Her mother conveyed the message that Jane wasn't capable of achieving that level of success, and she dissuaded her from pursuing a life dedicated to helping others.

One significant memory that shaped Jane's belief system was that bleak Christmas when Jane's mother blamed her for the family's being unable to afford a Christmas tree. From that, Jane derived the belief that she had the power to ruin people's lives. She felt like a walking curse. And when she felt the sting of being overlooked for birthdays and Christmas, she vowed she would never be so cruel to her own children in the future.

Jane's lack of confidence and unwillingness to take responsibility for her life no doubt led to feelings of hopelessness. With little else on which to focus, she became selfish and self-absorbed. She had a long life ahead of her; what would she do, and how would she survive? Convinced that working would get her nowhere, Jane resorted to a paralysis born of fatalism and negativity. Why expend a bunch of energy doing things that weren't going to work out anyway?

Desperate to find a purpose for her life, Jane sought direction and encouragement from her mother's own source of comfort: soap operas. These daily sagas drew Jane into a world of fantasy, which eventually overshadowed her dismal view of life. Her subsequent addiction to these unrealistic, drama-filled romances paved the way for her rescue-me way of thinking. At that point, the victim mentality was firmly in place.

## Revealing the Victim Mentality

The victim mentality says the perceived victim has no choice but to rely on others to meet her needs. The victim mindset is profoundly external in its function of control and encourages a person to believe she has neither the power nor the resources to change her life. The victim sees herself as optionless—perceiving life as grossly unfair. She simply cannot make important decisions concerning her life and therefore must wait for someone to make them for her.

Although this is by no means a comprehensive definition of the victim mentality, it adequately exposes Jane's mindset. Jane had no self-worth; consequently, she telegraphed a message that said, "Rescue me!" Once the "rescue me" message goes out, there will be no shortage of takers. As a matter of fact, after the first "rescuer" takes advantage of the "rescuee" or grows tired of the responsibility and moves on, there will be any number of people waiting in line to repeat the cycle. Although the attraction of rescuers to rescuees is almost irresistible, there could be no worse combination!

Jane's father had set the standard for what she expected in a man. She wanted a man who would show her unconditional love like her father had showed her mother. She expected a man to pamper her, cater to her every whim, provide for her, cook, clean, shop, and pay bills for her…and peel grapes and feed them to her while she watched soap operas.

Those are the types of fantasies entertained by young girls— and by adult women with little or no concept of reality. Basically, the only remotely appealing aspect of Jane's fantasy was the "help me; I'm all yours" part. Men who are attracted to that kitten-up-a-tree mindset are usually predators and abusers. These women tend to be dangerously gullible and trusting and therefore easy targets. A self-deceived abuser doesn't usually have to work hard to convince a woman with this mindset that he is, in fact, her long-awaited knight in shining armor.

Jane did set out to accomplish something on her own when she was a teenager. She pursued the only occupation for which she believed she was qualified at the time: modeling. It didn't require a whole lot of brainwork, just the ability to look good and move well. The outcome was not encouraging. The agency she signed with was engaging in work that only added more self-loathing to her already ailing identity. In order to "measure up," Jane had been required to do things that made her cringe with shame.

When shame was added to the mix, Jane, still a teenager, was more convinced than ever she was not capable of making her own decisions. By that time, she was well into her relationship with Daniel, who at first seemed to be her rescuer. Daniel had plans for his life—a foreign concept to Jane—but she set her sights on going along for the ride.

Daniel had his own issues, and Jane's chronic lack of self-worth was not one of them. He had acquired different attributes from his upbringing, and they in no way coincided with Jane's. He was athletic and did well in school. He was popular and in great demand by scores of girls and women. Daniel had a job and a flair for responsibility. About the only things he and Jane had in common were their physical attraction to each other and their love for nightlife and partying.

As far as Jane was concerned, Daniel was an exact match for the profile she had established for her rescuer. Unfortunately for her, however, Daniel had no immediate plans to take on that role. When they did get married—prematurely—Jane's immaturity and unrealistic expectations collided with Daniel's unresolved desires for other women and his love of freedom.

## Living the Legacy

History repeated itself when Daniel filed for divorce, leaving Jane pregnant with twins and with no way to support herself and their unborn children. Although Daniel was not physically abusive, Jane was re-traumatized by this abandonment. She miscarried the babies, and her world was shattered all over again.

Devastated, rejected, and desperate for stability with the man of her dreams, Jane subjected herself to unspeakable emotional torment in an effort to accomplish her goal. Her rescuer—the object of her affection—was the center of her world.

Unable to grasp the concept of personal growth or of seeking God to find out what He had in mind for her life, Jane continued to make the same mistakes women commonly make when we're lost and have no direction. Consumed with meeting her own needs, Jane threw caution, logic, and self-respect to the wind and concentrated on winning back the affections of her would-be rescuer. This course of action was a wild emotional ride for several years until the Lord dramatically intervened.

What follows is a rigorous analysis of Jane's mistakes. The discerning student will be warned by Jane's errors and apply the following lessons in their own lives.

## The Roots of Victim Thinking

What do you suppose were some attitudes and beliefs Jane carried over from her childhood that ultimately led to negative, victim-type behavior?

- Lack of education
- Poverty mentality
- Financial irresponsibility
- Lack of social skills
- Party mentality
- Lack of support system (friends, church, family)
- Godlessness
- Lack of motivation, goals, dreams
- No regard for achievement
- Guilt
- Rejection
- Defeatist attitude
- Lack of confidence
- Hopelessness
- Selfishness
- Laziness
- Desperation
- Drawn to fantasy
- Rescue-me mentality
- Victim mentality
- Children outside of marriage

Do you think Jane was a victim of her own mother's past?

If so, could she rightfully blame her mother and hold her responsible?

Do you think holding her mother responsible would have helped Jane in any way?

Would that change her past?

Would it change her mother's past?

How would holding someone else responsible change the future?

Whose responsibility is it to overcome the inherited victim mentality?

Should we accept negative attributes passed down to us from our parents and claim them as our heritage?

Section II

# Knowing the Truth
# Will Set You Free

—————◆—————

*The questions you discussed* in Section I were not trick questions, but the answer to each question that deals with blame is: It does not matter. The issue of blame is irrelevant, as far as God is concerned. Holding others responsible for our past is neither constructive nor important. The only significant aspect of our past is the part we can learn from as we grow up and move on. The past is behind us—so we can leave our blame in the past. The good news is that anyone can now start living the future God planned!

Perhaps you are at a crossroads right now. You've either been praying for a change—a way of escape—or perhaps someone has been praying for you. If that's not good news, how about this: You are alive! You may be battered and bruised on the inside and out. You may have suffered unimaginable abuse at the hands of a husband or boyfriend. But right now, you are receiving a wonderful gift. God has been waiting with great anticipation to tell you some truly exciting news!

Recovering your life and leaving your ugly, painful past behind will be a process—maybe a very long one. In fact, you may spend the rest of your life learning how to overcome your past and live in freedom and victory. This learning process is not punishment for taking a detour and "wasting your life." The process of overcoming the past is God's design for everyone—not just victims of abuse. You are now in the position to begin doing what God planned for you before you were even born.

## Message from God

The first thing God wants to communicate is that He loves you and He forgives you. If you have accepted Jesus Christ, the only Son of God, as your Lord and Savior, you have a get-out-of-jail-free pass. The Message Bible assures us:

> *"This is how much God loved the world: He gave his Son, his one and only Son. And this is why: so that no one need be destroyed;* by believing in him, anyone can have a whole and lasting life. *God didn't go to all the trouble of sending his Son merely to point an accusing finger, telling the world how bad it was. He came to help, to put the world right again.* Anyone who trusts in him is acquitted; *anyone who refuses to trust him has long since been under the death sentence without knowing it."* John 3:16–18 [Emphasis mine]

God is speaking to you. By believing in Jesus Christ, you are entitled to a whole and lasting life. This quality of life cannot be achieved alone, but only you can decide whether to accept God's most gracious and risk-free offer. When you do, you receive an Attorney for life—an Advocate who is always on your side. You are now free to walk out of your mental, emotional, and spiritual prison, a free woman.

If you have not yet accepted your paid-in-full gift of salvation and eternal life, you can do so now. It's simple. Romans 10:9–10 says:

> *"That if you confess with your mouth, 'Jesus is Lord,' and believe in your heart that God raised him from the dead, you will be saved. For it is with your heart that you believe*

*and are justified, and it is with your mouth that you confess and are saved." (NIV)*

Before we go any further, let's personalize God's offer to you. In your pre-printed journal, fill in the blanks with your own name and read it out loud until you are convinced that it's true.

> "This is how much God loved [your name]: He gave his Son, his one and only Son. And this is why: so that [your name] need not be destroyed; by believing in him, [your name] can have a whole and lasting life. God didn't go to all the trouble of sending his Son merely to point an accusing finger at [your name], telling her how bad she was. He came to help her, to put her right again. Because she trusts in him, [your name] is acquitted."

## God's Benefits Package

The benefits don't stop here. This is only the beginning. God has plenty more in store for you because He loves you and can't get enough of you! The only thing stopping Him from overwhelming you with blessings this very minute is His tenderness for your weak, frail humanity. It would be like plugging a toaster into a nuclear reactor. At this point in your life, you probably don't have much experience with unconditional love, blessings, and favor. You may need to warm up to God's goodness by first getting to know Him.

In Psalm 103:2–5 David celebrates these benefits we're talking about:

> *"Praise the Lord, O my soul, and forget not all his benefits—who forgives all your sins and heals all your diseases, who redeems your life from the pit and crowns you with love and compassion, who satisfies your desires with good things so that your youth is renewed like the eagle's." (NIV)*

It is doubtful that the blueprint of your background is just like Jane's, but it may be similar. If any or all of the generational issues previously mentioned have been a part of your life, you may consider yourself a victim. If you've been entrenched in the victim mindset, you may be convinced there is no hope for you. God wants you to know that there is hope for you, and lots of it!

Psalms 103:6 says, *"God makes everything come out right; he puts victims back on their feet."* (Message)

God says in Jeremiah 29:11, *"I know what I'm doing. I have it all planned out—plans to take care of you, not abandon you. Plans to give you the future you hope for."* (Message)

This is great news if you are genuinely ready for a life-changing relationship with God. He has a plan for you, and He knows what He's doing! He will not abandon you. He will give you the future you once hoped for, but had lost track of.

## Replace the Old Tapes with Truth

You probably need some time to absorb all this good news. You may have heard it before, but after what you've suffered, you need to hear it again…and again…and again. Having been intimate with an abusive partner, you are familiar with the power of words. Words have been used against you repeatedly to undermine your self-worth, your confidence, and your ability to survive outside the relationship.

Words can also be used to build you up. Hearing the Truth—and hearing it repeatedly—will be your greatest weapon against the lies spoken to you by the abuser.

The only way to erase those tapes in your mind is to replace them with tapes of Truth—the Word of God. God desperately wants you to know what He thinks and believes about you. It in no way coincides with the degrading and humiliating things you currently carry in your head. He doesn't see you the way you used to be or even how you are now. He sees you how you will be when you are perfected through Him. He is so pleased with what He sees; it's you…the way you were created to be!

God is not angry with you; He's not even disappointed. He is rejoicing that you have come to a place where the two of you can have an intimate relationship. Probably the most frustrating thing to Him when it concerns us is that our finite, messed-up minds prevent us from receiving all He wants to give us. If only we would believe and receive! In order to do that, we have to quit agreeing with the old tapes in our heads and start believing the Truth. He's even willing to help us with that!

We have a lot of work to do, but first let's make sure we're on the same page with what God wants to accomplish right now. Is any part of this section "news to you"? In order to make progress, it would be helpful to establish where you are in terms of your walk with God. If you've just read or heard any of these Scriptures for the first time, you may be wrestling with their validity. God understands that. The important thing is that you're willing to hear the Truth and that you trust Him to make it real in your life.

Keep in mind that the truth alone will not set you free, but knowing the Truth will! (John 8:32)

## Exercise

Take a few minutes to re-read this section, particularly the Scriptures. We're going to complete a short exercise, for which you will need highlighters of two different colors, a pen or pencil, and your journal.

In your pre-printed journal, highlight in one color those things you have already read or heard and recognize as Truth. These should be the things about which you have no doubts whatsoever. If you have your Bible, look up those Scriptures and highlight them there, as well. (Yes, it is okay to write in your Bible!) If your Bible is a different version than the Message or NIV, you will get even more insight as to what God is saying to you.

Write down the date next to these Scriptures, in both your journal and your Bible. This will help you chronicle your journey to wholeness!

Next, highlight in the second color those things you've either never read or heard or that you're simply not sure about. Again, highlight and date them in your Bible. In your journal, jot down the date and a personal note to God, asking Him to show you the Truth in a way you'll understand. He'll be thrilled to do it!

Write down any impressions or new thoughts. This is what your heart is "hearing" from God. If you don't receive anything at first, keep your spirit open for an answer. God loves to talk to his daughters—and He promises that we will hear His voice! When you do, write it in your journal, along with the date.

## Section III

# God Knows You Well

———————◆———————

*Hopefully, you are now* well on your way to believing that God loves you, He has a plan for you, and He's not mad at you or disappointed in you. Would it surprise you to know that He knew before you were born that you were going to be involved in the abusive relationship(s)? Even though He knew it, He didn't plan it, and it certainly wasn't His will for your life.

> *"Before I shaped you in the womb, I knew all about you.*
> *Before you saw the light of day, I had holy plans for you..."*
> Jeremiah 1:5 (Message)

Because God took such care in creating you, He knew ahead of time every move and every decision you would make. He didn't stop you because He gave you a free will and He always honors it. He did, however, plan around the detour you took because He will never give up on you. It is His desire that you be in good health and prosper, even as your soul prospers. (3 John 1:2)

## You Haven't Gone Too Far!

So what does this mean? It means you haven't messed up your life to the point of no return. You have received the first of many free gifts God has for you: You are on the path to restoration and freedom! Look at what He has to say to you right here and now:

> *"When you call on me, when you come and pray to me, I'll listen. When you come looking for me, you'll find me. Yes, when you get serious about finding me and want it more than anything else, I'll make sure you won't be disappointed."* GOD'S DECREE! *"I'll turn things around for you. I'll bring you back from all the countries into which I drove you"*— GOD'S DECREE—*"bring you home to the place from which I sent you off into exile. You can count on it."* Jeremiah 29:12–14 (Message)

Is that not the most amazing news you've heard in a long time? God is making this promise to you! He is saying that when you want to talk to Him, He will stop everything and give you His undivided attention. When you need to be in His presence, He'll make sure there's a place for you in His lap.

Is this promise too good to be true? Absolutely not. Is there a catch? Definitely. But it's a "catch" you can certainly live with. In order to activate God's promise to be available to you, you have to get serious about searching for Him. That means laying aside your own agenda. When you stop and think about it, it should not be that hard; look how we ended up when we took charge of our own lives!

## Wash Your Hands of the Past

How do you get serious about your walk with God? You have to completely wash your hands of your past. If you're not really at the end of your rope yet, perhaps you should set aside this study guide and come back to it when you are. God is committed to you one hundred per cent, and He wants the same from you.

God guarantees that if you want Him more than anything else and that if finding Him is your greatest priority, you will not be disappointed. Nobody else can even come close to giving you that kind of guarantee, and His won't cost you a dime. It will, however, cost you your life. But the life you surrender to Him will be returned shiny and new and will be accompanied by hope and a future!

> *"If you don't go all the way with me, through thick and thin, you don't deserve me. If your first concern is to look after yourself, you'll never find yourself. But if you forget about yourself and look to me, you'll find both yourself and me."*
> Matthew 10:38–39 (Message)

## Exercise

Before we go any further, please take this opportunity to search your heart and decide whether or not you are serious about exchanging your old life for a brand-new one. This means you must be willing to say goodbye to the "rescue me; I'm a victim" mentality. If you are certain you are ready for this kind of commitment, write in your journal a personal declaration to God that you are finished calling all the shots and that you trust Him to clean up the mess, pick up the pieces, and restore you and your life.

If you are still mourning the loss of your abusive relationship, write that down as well. Be brutally honest; this is no time for self-deception. That's what landed you in the situation in the first place. The goal is to identify what is real and what is fantasy. Until you get revelation about this, you're destined to keep re-living your past.

Jane managed to convince herself that if she didn't say it out loud, it wasn't really true. She was able to deflect the reality of her situation, and all her responsibility for it, until she actually started saying it out loud. If you are still in the stage of not wanting to acknowledge the truth about your abusive relationship, please take all the time you need to pray about it. If you still believe you had nothing to do with your situation, at least be willing to question yourself and find out for sure.

Jane was unwilling to do without the physical intimacy and sexual contact her relationship offered. That aspect of her relationship with her abusive husband was so important to her that she had allowed herself to be blinded to her own needs and the needs of her children.

What are you unwilling to do without? What is keeping you entrenched in an unhealthy relationship? What is it that keeps your foot nailed to the floor as you go around and around in circles?

Your list may go something like this:

- I miss the way he "encouraged" me to be a better person.
- I miss the way he made me feel physically.
- I miss the way he "protected" me from friends and family members who did not have my best interests at heart.
- I miss the way he kept me from "spoiling" my kids and thereby not allowing them to become dependent little bums.

Make a complete list. Take all the time you need. The more thorough you are, the more successfully you can break with the past and enter into a new life. When you finish your list, take a long, thoughtful look at it. Are these some of the reasons you allowed the abuse to continue? Were you convinced that, down deep, he had your best interests at heart?

All of the things you wrote down may have made sense to you while you were in the relationship. They may still make sense to you. However, your perception needs to change, or the chances of your regaining control of your own life are slim to none. If your list still sounds reasonable, the abuser still holds the keys to your heart and your mind.

Maybe you're still not sure. If you still have doubts but would genuinely like to be ready for a new life, make a list of your doubts and concerns and ask God to work with you. He already knows what your struggles are; He just wants you to bring them to Him and ask Him to help you. Isn't that what good fathers do? God is not just a good Father; He's the best. He won't turn you down. As a matter of fact, right now He is excited to meet you as you come to Him with your doubts, failures, and fears.

# The Power of Agreement

*There is a power* on this earth and in the spirit realm that is far greater than the power any one person can have over another. It is the power of agreement, and it has to do with the words we speak and the things we believe. It is so powerful, in fact, that heaven, earth, and all of eternity are affected when two or more come into agreement.

> *"Take this most seriously: A yes on earth is yes in heaven; a no on earth is no in heaven. What you say to one another is eternal. I mean this. When two of you get together on anything at all on earth and make a prayer of it, my Father in heaven goes into action. And when two or three of you are together because of me, you can be sure that I'll be there."*
> Matthew 18:19–20 (Message)

What does this have to do with your situation? Everything. You found yourself in—or stayed in—an abusive relationship because you agreed with what someone else said about you. One of the primary strategies of a captor is to wear down and undermine the confidence of the captive so that she wouldn't escape even if given a chance. It's a learned behavior to which even animals respond.

## Psychological Barriers

For instance, if an elephant is chained to a stake and is struck every time it tries to break free, it will come to believe the stake has the power to hold it captive. Even though the elephant possesses more than enough strength to either break the chain or to pull the stake out of the ground, it is physically manipulated into thinking that the power to hold it down belongs to something outside of itself.

After a while, the mere memory of being struck will keep the elephant from attempting to escape. It will walk in the circular pattern around the stake even if the threat of being struck no longer exists. The bondage is not on the outside; it is in the elephant's mind.

The same applies to the principle of putting a shock collar on a dog and administering a painful but non-lethal shock when the dog tries to go past an invisible fence. The dog can't even see the fence, so the fence isn't really the problem. It's what happens when it approaches the fence that causes it to experience pain. If the dog knew the shocking would cease once it got past the invisible barrier and out of the range of the transmitter, chances are it would be off and running, maybe never to return.

In essence, the elephant and the dog have been subdued by psychological restraints. That is often the case in an abusive relationship. A woman is so conditioned to believing threats, accusations, and insults, and/or being struck that if she does get a chance to bolt, the psychological barriers often override her ability to escape. A momentary opportunity is not usually long enough for the psychologically abused woman to assess the situation and believe that freedom is a real possibility. In many cases, the woman feels just as imprisoned as the mighty elephant tethered to a small stake by a chain.

How does this happen? Simply put, it has to do with the power of agreement. Whereas the aforementioned Scripture emphasizes the positive power of agreement—it also works in reverse. If we believe and agree that we cannot make it on our own, that we are not worthy of a good life, that there is no way of escape—then that will become our reality.

## Beliefs Become Faith

If we believe in something we cannot see, it is called faith. Faith does not pertain to just our belief in the things of God. It also applies to what we believe about ourselves, others, our position in life, etc. If we agree that God is good and that He has good plans for our life, that is how our faith will be established. We will walk in that belief and it will become a reality.

But if we believe we are useless, stupid, fat, lazy, ugly, etc., those beliefs become our faith. It's a negative faith, to be sure, but faith nevertheless. It's not faith in God, obviously, because those beliefs are in direct contrast to what He says about us. No one in her right mind would deliberately agree with Satan, God's enemy, but that's exactly what happens when we agree with anything about ourselves, others, or our position in life that does not line up with what God says.

It is extremely rare that Satan shows up personally to say all the hideous things we sometimes believe about ourselves. These things almost always come via someone with whom we have a relationship. In Jane's case, most of the negative things she originally came to believe about herself were delivered by her mother's mouth. Because her mother gave birth to her, raised her, and "knew" her, Jane assumed that what her mother said was right. She agreed with those things. They became her beliefs, which became her faith. Before long, they became her reality and identity.

By the time beliefs become faith, our identities have been established in the process. Short of a profound change, we will then live the rest of our lives in accordance with that identity. If the beliefs are false, our identities are false. False identities do not change by chance. First they have to be identified, then the lies have to be exchanged for the Truth—what God says about us.

27

## Identifying False Beliefs

The first step to exchanging lies for the Truth is to identify the lies or false beliefs. When Jane's mother told her that the family didn't have a Christmas tree because Jane had been a bad girl, was that the truth? To a full-grown adult, that statement would be dismissed as ludicrous. But to an innocent little girl, it had to be true. Why would her own mother have said it if it weren't true?

Actions and events can reinforce beliefs as well. Jane struggled with a lifelong addiction to food. When, as an adult, she made a concerted effort to learn about food and about her body, she was able to temporarily override the things she originally believed. But when her circumstances changed and she lost her confidence, Jane resorted to power eating, which means eating lots of food really quickly. When she did so habitually, she lost control of her weight again.

After praying and fasting, God revealed to Jane that the experience of watching her family's refrigerator being repossessed as a little girl caused her to fear that there would not be enough food in the house. Whether the thought came from the enemy or was a reasonable assumption for a traumatized little girl to make, Jane incorporated that thought into her belief system.

From that time on, Jane operated with the unconscious belief that there would never be enough food. As a result, she tended to eat unusually large quantities of food at a time and did so with blinding speed. When she finally realized that she was "inhaling" her food for no apparent reason, she began to question what was behind her actions. When Jane became aware of the lie that had perpetuated the behavior, she immediately broke agreement with the lie.

## Agree with the Truth

Just breaking agreement with a person or a lie is not enough. You must replace the agreement with one of Truth. What does God say about young Jane's perceived shortage of food? *"And my*

*God will supply all your needs according to His riches in glory in Christ Jesus."* Philippians 4:19 (NAS)

When Jane was a little girl, she didn't know that God promised to supply all her needs, including food. But as an adult, she could believe He would. After she broke agreement with the lie that she would not have enough food, Jane agreed with God's Word, which says He will supply all her needs. As she continues to declare the Truth out loud, she will come to believe without doubting, and that will become her faith, which will produce her reality.

> *"Consequently, faith comes from hearing the message, and the message is heard through the word of Christ."* Romans 10:17 (NIV)

Faith is active; it sets things into motion. The power of God responds to your faith. Matthew 9:29–30 says, *"He touched their eyes and said, 'Become what you believe.' It happened. They saw."* (Message) Make sure your faith is based on and agrees with the Truth.

## Exercise

We have lots of work to do. Here's where your past is going to come in handy. Did you ever think that could happen? We're going to view your upbringing as a blueprint for your wrong thinking and beliefs. This is not going to be an assignment you can zip through in just a few minutes. It will take some deep thought and unfettered honesty. If at all possible, set aside a block of time in a place where you are least likely to be disturbed.

We're going to begin by establishing a family history of sorts. This will be an insightful and emotional journey. This exercise will guide you through some general questions about your family of origin. To the best of your ability, write down what you know about both your mother's and father's side of the family. Make sure you separate the information for each parent. The next section will deal with the information you produce as a result of this exercise.

So take your time and be as accurate and as open-minded as possible.

If your biological parents were your primary caretakers, you will probably know enough about them to give you significant insight into your current situation. If you don't know these things off-hand, ask other family members, if possible. The goal of this exercise is to reveal generational patterns that may have ultimately led to your abusive relationship. The purpose of uncovering this information is not to cast blame or to make excuses. It is to show you where and how generational weaknesses and events have contributed to creating your false identity.

If your biological parents were not your primary caretakers, include what, if anything, you know about their background, but also provide the same information for your primary caretakers (grandparents, adoptive or foster parents, other family members, etc.).

Before you start, pray and ask God to give you the grace and strength to do this and to show you the lies you believe about yourself. Use the following questions to get started. They may lead to other thoughts, feelings, or ideas. Journal one by one, in peace and grace, without striving.

Was your mom/dad poor or wealthy? What were your mom's/dad's thoughts about money? What was said in your household about money?

Was your mom/dad sick or healthy? Was there injury, illness, trauma in your mom's/dad's life?

Was there early death or suicide on either side of the family?

Violence? Mental illness?

Divorce? Infidelity? Perversion? Incest? Pornography? Out-of-wedlock pregnancy? Abortion?

Drug or alcohol addictions?

Hatred or prejudice?

# Understanding the Cycle of Abuse

*Hopefully, the information you* provided for the previous exercise has already paved the way for some new understanding about your own caretakers. It is unusual for people in abusive relationships to have had a stable, healthy childhood. Typically, women who end up in abusive relationships have learned somewhere along the line that they don't deserve better.

You probably have plenty of negative tapes playing in your head regarding all your shortcomings. Those tapes represent a lifetime of events you've experienced and words that have been spoken to you, about you, and around you. If you grew up witnessing abuse or being abused, you may never have known that another life was possible. Depending on the situation, you may have learned or assumed that the abuse was your fault. That made you a prime candidate to attract the type of person who would help you perpetuate the cycle.

## What's on Your Tapes?

Let's take a "look" at the tapes in your head. Over the course of your lifetime, you have experienced hundreds of thousands of events that have contributed to your outlook on life. Some of those events are tucked "safely" in your unconscious mind, where they remain undetected. Other events made such a profound impact in your life that you may think about them all day, every day. A significant event may involve the death of a loved one, a violent assault, a tragic accident, witnessing a violent or tragic event, a nasty divorce, a near-death experience, prolonged sickness, a serious handicap, etc.

Just as harmful as physical trauma may be some of the words you heard when you were a child. Words can be as powerful as physical blows to the body; they just don't produce bruises or bleeding on the outside. However, the bruises and bleeding in the soul—our mind, will, and emotions—can be damaged just as badly, if not more so. Many times, certain words and memories constitute their very own tape that plays in our minds over and over again. No matter where we are or what we're doing, those tapes are playing in the background and have a profound effect on our everyday lives.

Hopefully, you have not been so seriously damaged that professional help is required, but if that is the case, by all means seek the help you need. This book is not the final cure for anything that ails you. However, God is more than capable of picking you up, dusting you off, and breathing new life into you. If you have gotten this far in the book, you probably believe that by now! He's waiting for you to take the next step because He has so many things to show you. Emotional pain will probably be involved, but the healing and deliverance He has in store for you are not only worth the pain, but are more valuable than a bucket of gold!

## The Pain behind the Behavior

One thing God wants to show you now is that the people who hurt you were dealing with their own hurt, unresolved guilt, shame, and grief. That doesn't excuse their behavior; however, a little understanding goes a long way. In Jane's case, she thought her mother was mean, hateful, lazy, and selfish. Even though she was able to forgive her for having said and done some unspeakably hurtful things, Jane never knew the reason behind her mother's behavior until we wrote the book.

When she observed her mother's sad countenance as she recalled her own painful childhood, Jane experienced a rush of compassion for her. Just knowing those things about her mother made it easier for Jane to not only forgive her but to befriend her.

It is likely that the person(s) who hurt you the most was the one who had also suffered the most. Could it be that he or she never had the "luxury" you now have of being healed and delivered? Would it surprise you to know that while you are replaying the tapes of what that person said and did to you, you are unconsciously reliving those things and are probably saying and doing the same to someone you love? Think about it: If your mother was unbearably critical of you and constantly belittled you, you may have already begun the same cycle in your own child's life.

If that's true, you've probably justified your behavior by saying or thinking, *That's what my mother said and did to me!* What if your own mother said the same thing about her mother? Are you seeing a pattern here? These are generational cycles that will continue in full force and effect until you agree to put an end to them. You obviously have no power over the past, but you certainly have what it takes to change your present and your future. And when you do, you will automatically change the lives of generations ahead of you. Now *that's* power!

## Exercise

In this exercise you will need a long, blank sheet of paper and some pens with different colored ink. We will construct a timeline of the events and words that have so profoundly affected you and may have contributed to your part in the abusive relationship.

First, draw a straight line across the paper. Put the date you were born at the left and begin with the earliest memory you can recall. Write down what you remember of what was said and who said it. Record the year and the date if you can remember. You can write both positive and negative events, but write them in different colors. For example, Jane's timeline contains an entry for "Christmas, 1964" that says "No Christmas tree. Mother said it was my fault." What will emerge is a picture of your reality before you ever got involved in an abusive relationship.

Once you've completed the timeline, take time to pray and ask God to show you what He wants you to see about each thing you have recorded. Write these insights in your journal and date them as well. Revelation may not come all at once. If God wakes you in the middle of the night and shows you something, be diligent to write it down then. Chances are, you won't remember it as clearly in the morning, and you don't want to miss a single detail.

Section VI

# The Power of Forgiveness

—◆—

*After looking at the* timeline of our lives, I think we can agree that the identity we were operating in was not the one God had planned for us. Are you willing to "trade in" your old, false identity for a brand-new one that has a future and is full of hope?

If you genuinely want to exchange your old life for a new one, but you still want to be in charge of the changes, you simply are not at the end of your rope yet. It may be a trust issue because you've been hurt and betrayed too many times. If that's the case, pray and ask God to soften your heart and to get you to the point of total surrender. He knows what you've been through and how wounded you are. He is far greater than your problems and is more than willing to help you with this process.

## Out with the Old, in with the New

When you are ready to begin the process of exchanging your old way of living and thinking for a brand-new life and an exciting new perspective on it, God has a word of encouragement for you:

*"Therefore, if anyone is in Christ, he is a new creation; the old has gone, the new has come!"* 2 Corinthians 5:17 (NIV)

The instant you ask Jesus Christ to be your Lord and Savior, you become a new creation in Him. You are "born again." You have a clean slate. Do you magically change from one person into another when you are born again? No more so than if someone deposited several million dollars into your bank account and you chose to ignore it. In both cases, it's there for you; you just have to tap into it.

One of the first and most important aspects of becoming a new creation is that of developing a forgiving nature. Jesus died so that every person ever created could be forgiven of his or her sins and have a place with Him in eternity. It doesn't cost us anything but our lives! By that, we have to be willing to exchange our old sinful nature and accept the righteousness we now have in Him. We are now in right standing with God. In order to live the life He planned for each of us before time began, we must be willing to take on His character. One of those character attributes is that of forgiveness.

## Forgiveness is not Optional

Forgiveness is not a single event, it is not a conditional thing, and it is not optional. In fact, if we do not forgive those who hurt us and trespass against us, our Father in heaven will not forgive us. The parable of the king and the servant in Matthew 18:21–35 makes clear God's view of unforgiveness:

> "At that point Peter got up the nerve to ask, 'Master, how many times do I forgive a brother or sister who hurts me? Seven?' Jesus replied, 'Seven! Hardly. Try seventy times seven. The kingdom of God is like a king who decided to square accounts with his servants. As he got under way, one servant was brought before him who had run up a debt of a hundred thousand dollars. He couldn't pay up, so the king ordered the man, along with this wife, children, and goods, to be auctioned off at the slave market. The poor wretch threw

*himself at the king's feet and begged, 'Give me a chance and I'll pay it all back.' Touched by his plea, the king let him off, erasing the debt. The servant was no sooner out of the room when he came upon one of his fellow servants who owed him ten dollars. He seized him by the throat and demanded, 'Pay up. Now!' The poor wretch threw himself down and begged, 'Give me a chance and I'll pay it all back.' But he wouldn't do it. He had him arrested and put in jail until the debt was paid. When the other servants saw this going on, they were outraged and brought a detailed report to the king. The king summoned the man and said, 'You evil servant!* I forgave your entire debt when you begged me for mercy. *Shouldn't you be compelled to be merciful to your fellow servant who asked for mercy?' The king was furious and put the screws to the man until he paid back his entire debt.* And that's exactly what my Father in heaven is going to do to each one of you who doesn't forgive unconditionally anyone who asks for mercy.'" (Message) [Emphasis mine]

Some of us have been so betrayed and wounded we believe it's impossible to forgive the one(s) who hurt us. If God says to do it, it is possible. It's not only possible, it's mandatory.

God paid an incredible price so that our sins could be forgiven. The least we can do in return is to forgive others when they hurt us. One of the most obvious consequences of harboring unforgiveness is found in verse 35. God won't forgive us if we don't forgive others. On the other hand, He will forgive us if we do forgive others.

## Forgiveness is about Empowerment

Forgiveness is not about denying that another person hurt or betrayed you. That person may have committed a heinous and atrocious crime against you, in which case, you couldn't "fix" it if you spent the rest of your life trying.

Forgiveness is about empowerment. If we don't forgive, we automatically fall into the "victim" category, and victims do not operate from a position of power. As long as someone remains a victim, she can expect to stay at a distinct disadvantage until she decides to forgive.

Jesus is the only person in the history of creation who willingly allowed Himself to become a human sacrifice (and who was in the position to do so!) so that others could bypass an eternity in hell. But let's say He emerged from the tomb on the third day, railing against God for having allowed His death. What if He spent the next two thousand years calling to our attention that we were the low-life sinners who caused His death? Not only would we not accept Jesus' "sacrifice," we would avoid Him at all costs. After all, we can be berated and condemned in our own households and at our own jobs!

More important, Jesus would have no power. He would have been the victim, and victims are always at someone else's mercy. God wants to empower you so you can represent Him well. He wants to show off through you by rescuing you from a "hopeless" situation, cleaning you up, and dressing you up like the royalty you were created to be. He wants you to be able to operate from a standpoint of the power and authority that came with your salvation, free of charge.

With an offer like that, we would be fools to want to hang on to our victim mentality. It just doesn't make sense! We are heirs to everything God has, if we'll accept who we are in Him and will live the life He planned for us all along.

You now have organized information concerning the people who hurt you and the offenses committed against you. The first step toward exchanging your old life for the brand-new one God has waiting for you is to forgive each one of those people. If you believe you simply cannot do that, take a step of faith and tell God, "Lord, you know I want to be able to do this, but I just can't.

Help me to want to forgive." He will honor your prayer. He wants you to be set free even more than you do!

## Exercise

Commit to God that with His help, you are going to forgive those who have hurt you and trespassed against you. Then make a list of each person against whom you harbor unforgiveness. Write next to each name the "nature" of his or her offense against you.

That was the easy part. Next is the real test: Say out loud, "Lord, I confess with my mouth that I forgive [name of person] for [offense]. I'm asking You to help my heart to back up what I just confessed."

You may have to repeat the process several times and possibly for several weeks. But you can and will learn to forgive and to trust God to take care of the justice part.

If you're still feeling like this is an impossible task, keep this in mind: You have trespassed against and offended others many times during the course of your life. Do you ever want to hear from your child's mouth or the mouth of someone else whom you dearly love, "I'll never forgive you as long as I live!"? The quickest way to steer clear of judgment against you is not to judge others.

> "Do not judge so that you will not be judged. For in the way you judge, you will be judged; and by your standard of measure, it will be measured to you. Why do you look at the speck that is in your brother's eye, but do not notice the log that is in your own eye? Or how can you say to your brother, 'Let me take the speck out of your eye,' and behold, the log is in your own eye? You hypocrite, first take the log out of your own eye, and then you will see clearly to take the speck out of your brother's eye." Matthew 7:1–5 (NAS)

Congratulations! You are now ready for the grand finale of this exercise. You have come a long way in a short period of time, and you have the power and strength to do this.

The last two people you need to forgive are God and yourself. You may be thinking that you don't harbor unforgiveness toward God, or maybe you can't even imagine such a thing. But many times, we tell ourselves in the midst of painful times that if God really loved us, He wouldn't allow awful things to happen to us. Remember that any evil directed your way was not God's will for you. We live in a fallen world where both the evil and the good have their own free will.

God doesn't need your forgiveness for Himself; He's big enough to take whatever you can dish out. He wants to empower you to live a life of favor, blessings, and abundance. Unforgiveness will hinder His plans for you.

Last but not least, you must forgive yourself for failing, hurting, and disappointing loved ones and even yourself. When Jesus said, "Do not judge so that you will not be judged," He meant that you are not to judge yourself any more than you are to judge someone else. His work on the cross was complete. There are no loopholes or exceptions. Whatever you have said or done can—and will—be forgiven. Simply confess your sins and ask your heavenly Father to forgive you. It's a done deal.

> *"If we confess our sins, He is faithful and righteous to forgive us our sins and to cleanse us from all unrighteousness."* 1 John 1:9 (NAS)

As the last step of this exercise, make a list of the things you are aware of having said or done that have hurt or offended others. If possible, approach those people personally and humbly ask for their forgiveness. When that's not possible, make a phone call or write a letter. If that person is deceased, simply speak it out loud and consider yourself forgiven. In most cases, people will be so touched by your humility, they won't hesitate to forgive you. If not, just know that you did what you're supposed to do, and trust God to change some hearts!

## Section VII

# Discover Your God-Designed Identity

---

*Let's look at what* you've accomplished so far in your journey to break free from a victim mentality:

- By looking closely at your family history, you have discovered the generational patterns that have affected your thoughts, behavior, and decisions.

- You are aware of the words spoken to you as well as the events that profoundly impacted your life prior to your abusive relationship.

- You have learned that agreeing with false statements and beliefs established your faith, which led you to assume a false identity.

- You now know that forgiveness is necessary in order to break free from the victim mentality and to discover your God-designed identity and the future He planned for you before you were born.

What you have learned about yourself are the things that, when put together into a package, constituted an identity that attracted the mate who ended up abusing you. You have just consumed a hefty chunk of the elephant! You are now ready to say goodbye to the false identity that got you into the situation you are now breaking free from.

Now you are aware of your own characteristics and false beliefs that contributed to the attraction between you and the man who abused you. Your false beliefs and false identity combined with the abusive personality of your significant other created a dangerous and potentially deadly recipe. Now that you are making a clean break with the past, and you recognize the triggers of victim behaviors, you are well-equipped to avoid abusive relationships in the future.

Let's continue on the path of discovering your God-designed identity. Recall your timeline exercise from Section V. Review in your journal the words and events that you agreed with and that led you to assume a false identity. You have learned that by agreeing with something, you form beliefs. Those beliefs become your faith. Your faith then produces your reality. Now we are going to learn how to break those agreements and replace them with new agreements.

## What Does God Say About You?

First, let's take a look at what God says about you, your life, and your relationship with Him. The following Scriptures are paraphrased for easier understanding:

> *There is nothing I don't know about you.* (Psalm 139:1)
>
> *I made you in My image.* (Genesis 1:27)
>
> *You are My child.* (Acts 17:28)
>
> *I knew you before you were conceived; you were My idea.* (Jeremiah 1:5)
>
> *I chose you when I planned creation.* (Ephesians 1:11)
>
> *Nothing about you is a mistake; I carefully crafted every part of you.* (Psalm 139:15)

*I know what you're going to do each day; your days are recorded in My book.* (Psalm 139:16)

*I decided exactly when you would be born and where you would live.* (Acts 17:26)

*I know exactly how you were made; I crafted you Myself.* (Psalm 139:14)

*I decided every last detail about you—inside and out—from the time you were conceived.* (Psalm 139:13)

*When you were fully formed, I called you forth from your mother's womb.* (Psalm 71:6)

*I am not distant and angry; I am the perfect and complete expression of love.* (1 John 4:16)

*I long to consume you with My love because you are My child and I am your Father.* (1 John 3:1)

*Your earthly father cannot come close to giving you what I can.* (Matthew 7:11)

*I am the perfect Father in every way.* (Matthew 5:48)

*Every time you receive a good gift, know it's from Me.* (James 1:17)

*Don't worry about how you will survive; I know all your needs. Look to Me first and I will take care of you.* (Matthew 6:31–33)

*Choose My plan for your future; it is full of hope.* (Jeremiah 29:11)

*I have never quit loving you and I never will.* (Jeremiah 31:3)

*My thoughts of you outnumber the grains of sand on the seashore; you are always on My mind!* (139:17–18)

*I celebrate you by singing over you.* (Zephaniah 3:17)

*My mind is made; I will never stop doing good to you.* (Jeremiah 32:40)

*You are My special treasure.* (Exodus 19:5)

*I will stick with you no matter what; I will be so good to you, you won't even consider turning away from Me.* (Jeremiah 32:41)

*I'll tell you marvelous and wondrous things that you could never figure out on your own.* (Jeremiah 33:3)

*If you seek Me with everything you have, you will find Me.* (Deuteronomy 4:29)

*Delight yourself in Me and I will give you your heart's desires.* (Psalm 37:4)

*For it is I who gave you those desires.* (Philippians 2:13)

*On your best day, you cannot imagine all that I can do for you!* (Ephesians 3:20)

*I am your greatest fan and will never stop helping and encouraging you.* (2 Thessalonians 2:16–17)

*When you are having trouble, look for Me; I will be there to comfort you.* (2 Corinthians 1:3–4)

*When you are brokenhearted, I am right next to you.* (Psalm 34:18)

*Like a good shepherd carries a lamb, I have carried you next to My heart.* (Isaiah 40:11)

*One day, I will wipe away all of your tears and you will no longer cry, be sad, or feel pain.* (Revelation 21:3–4)

*I am your Father and I love you in the same way I love My Son, Jesus.* (John 17:23)

*I am on your side; you cannot lose!* (Romans 8:31)

*I'm not keeping track of your sins and mistakes.* (2 Corinthians 5:19)

*Through Me, you can conquer any and every thing that opposes you.* (Romans 8:37)

*Nothing on heaven or earth can separate you from My love.* (Romans 8:38–39)

You may never have heard the Truth before. Even if you have, you need to hear it over and over until it gets into your spirit and you believe it wholeheartedly. Remember, when you believe something, it becomes your faith. Your faith then produces your reality. The Truth is a much greater and wiser investment than the negative beliefs that have kept you in bondage to a victim mentality. Wouldn't you agree?

## Exercise

Review your list of false beliefs (lies) that contributed to the victim mentality you are now relinquishing. Replace each false belief with the Truth—what God says about you. For example, if one of your false beliefs is that you were a mistake, look to see what God says, and write it down.

Truth:

*There is nothing I don't know about you.* (Psalm 139:1)

*I made you in My image.* (Genesis 1:27)

*You are My child.* (Acts 17:28)

*I knew you before you were conceived; you were My idea.* (Jeremiah 1:5)

*I chose you when I planned creation.* (Ephesians 1:11)

*Nothing about you is a mistake; I carefully crafted every part of you.* (Psalm 139:15)

*I know what you're going to do each day; your days are recorded in My book.* (Psalm 139:16)

*I decided exactly when you would be born and where you would live.* (Acts 17:26)

*I know exactly how you were made; I sculpted you Myself.* (Psalm 139:14)

*I decided every last detail about you—inside and out—from the time you were conceived.* (Psalm 139:13)

*When you were fully formed, I called you forth from your mother's womb.* (Psalm 71:6)

If you believed the lie that you are not capable of surviving on your own, write down the Truth:

*Don't worry about how you will survive; I know all your needs. Look to Me first and I will take care of you.* (Matthew 6:31–33)

*Choose My plan for your future; it is full of hope.* (Jeremiah 29:11)

*I will stick with you no matter what; I will be so good to you, you won't even consider turning away from Me.* (Jeremiah 32:41)

*I'll tell you marvelous and wondrous things that you could never figure out on your own.* (Jeremiah 33:3)

*If you seek Me with everything you have, you will find Me.* (Deuteronomy 4:29)

*Delight yourself in Me and I will give you your heart's desires.* (Psalm 37:4)

*For it is I who gave you those desires.* (Philippians 2:13)

*On your best day, you cannot imagine all that I can do for you!* (Ephesians 3:20)

*I am your greatest fan and will never stop helping and encouraging you.* (2 Thessalonians 2:16–17)

*I am on your side; you cannot lose!* (Romans 8:31)

*Through Me you can conquer any and every thing that opposes you.* (Romans 8:37)

After you have replaced the false beliefs with God's Truth, you will be well on your way to burying your past and moving fullspeed ahead with His hope-filled plan for you. Now it's time to break agreement with all the lies you have believed about yourself, your life, who you are and whom you were meant to be. For each false belief say out loud, "I break agreement with the lie that says...."

For example, if one of the false beliefs was, "I was a mistake," simply say, "I break agreement with the lie that I was a mistake." Take your pen and mark through that lie. Next, say out loud, "I agree with the Truth. God says...." Simply repeat all the Truth that replaces that lie, i.e., "I agree with the Truth that there is nothing that God doesn't know about me. I agree that I was made in His image and that I am His child." Highlight each one as you say it.

Once you've completed this exercise, those false beliefs will be dead and buried, but it will still be helpful to hear the Truth day after day. There is something about speaking it aloud that more fully engages our hearts and solidifies our new belief system. Your false identity is now dead. Make a commitment to yourself that you will not "raise it from the dead!" From now on, all you are going to believe is what God says about you, your life, and who you are in Him. Once again, what you believe becomes your faith. Your faith then produces your reality. Let no one dissuade you from believing the Truth.

You are in the midst of a lifelong journey. That doesn't mean you won't see any results until you "get there." On the contrary, it means every day from now on will be full of hope and excitement because you will be walking in Truth, right alongside the Truth Himself—Jesus Christ.

This process is referred to as "renewing your mind." This is the process by which you will continue to shed your old, false identity and walk into your new, God-designed identity.

> *"And do not be conformed to this world, but be transformed by the renewing of your mind, so that you may prove what the will of God is, that which is good and acceptable and perfect."* Romans 12:2 (NAS)

# Own Your Actions and Decisions

———————◆———————

*So far, we have* addressed the parts of your past that have contributed to a victim mentality. That mentality led you to behave and
make decisions in accordance with false beliefs. Those beliefs became your faith, and your faith became your reality.

We have dealt primarily with issues from your past, prior to
the abusive relationship. Painful as it may be, it is important to see
those things about yourself and your history, in order to own or
take responsibility for your part in the situation. That is not to say
or imply that what happened to you was entirely your fault. It
means that if you don't see what drew you into the situation or
how you contributed to it, you are still functioning out of a victim
mentality.

The only way you can take ownership of your life and move
ahead is to acknowledge your failures and mistakes and learn from
them. Stop playing the blame game. There is no power in that. In
order to move into the future God planned for you before you
were born, you must operate from a position of power—not your
power, but His. As long as you continue to give credit and power
to your abuser, you are hindering God from moving on your be-

half. He needs to have complete access to you and your situation in order to heal and restore you.

## Accelerated Restoration

Although the abusive relationship may have consumed years of your life, God is excited about quickly restoring those lost years back to you. This is a season of acceleration. What used to take years to accomplish in the spirit realm is now taking considerably less time. That's how serious God is about dusting you off and moving you into His plan for your future.

Your spirit and soul (mind, will, and emotions) may not be the only things that were damaged in the relationship. You also may have suffered or continue to suffer serious physical injuries and financial devastation. There is no way to minimize your pain and loss; that's not the point of this study guide.

The goal is for you to see yourself through God's eyes and to get His perspective on your situation. He is fiercely protective of you, and as long as you depend on Him to rescue, avenge, and restore you, you can be assured that He will do it. Just make sure you don't surrender everything, only to take back bits and pieces to handle on your own. It doesn't work that way.

In Jane's case, she was not the only one who suffered from the abuse. Her three daughters were not only subjected to psychological and verbal abuse, but were robbed of their college education as well. In addition, they lost their home, financial security, and the stability of a healthy, functioning family.

A lot of damage was done, but God is a big God. In a short period of time, He has pulled Jane and her daughters out of the pit and has set them on solid ground. He has enabled them all to forgive the abuser and each other. Jane and her girls are back on track with God and are moving into the hope-filled future He had planned for them all along.

The key to God's being able to move on their behalf is that Jane was willing to "own" her part in the situation and to subsequently surrender the entire mess to Him. She was gradually able to let go of every word, thought, and deed pertaining to the abuse and to trust completely that God is able and willing to do what He promises.

The more freedom Jane gave to God, the more He was able to move on her behalf. This type of ownership and surrender will be required of you as well.

## God Sees the Whole Picture

God knows every detail of what happened to you and your loved ones as a result of the abusive relationship. He is even more grieved about your pain and suffering than you are. The difference is, He sees the whole picture, and you see only a small part. What He sees in you now is not the broken-down, abused you; He sees the glorious, victorious woman of God He created you to be.

God is also an individual God. Your healing and restoration will be as unique as you are. He may take a different and unpredictable approach in your situation, and He may require from you some unusual things. You will have to walk closely with Him to "hear" and understand what He is saying.

One thing for sure is that you will be required to forgive the abuser in order to break free from the victim mentality. If not, you will not be able to move forward. You must also break your agreement with the lies that are recorded on the tapes in your mind. In addition, you will be required to replace those lies with Truth, to create new tapes like you did in the previous sections. There are many on-ramps to this avenue of accelerated restoration. God will lead you to the one that is most effective and the best fit for you.

## Exercise

Write a letter to God, pouring out your heart to Him about your pain, shame, disappointment, etc. He doesn't care about your grammar or even your language. He just wants your heart. As He helps you, commit to Him to surrender every last detail of the ordeal. Tell Him you trust Him to rescue, avenge, and restore you. Confess that you forgive the abuser, even if you don't mean it just yet. Ask God to help your heart to back it up.

You don't have to record every lie and event with which you agreed during this time of your life. You did that in a previous exercise. This exercise is simply for you to pour out to God the emotion of your heart. Ask God in your letter to erase those tapes in your mind by His power. Tell Him that you no longer agree with what His enemy says about you; from now on you will believe only the Truth. Ask God to remind you of the Truth every time one of those lies comes to mind.

Tell God you are ready to bury your old identity so you can walk into the new, God-designed identity He has waiting for you. End your letter by addressing anything else that concerns you.

When you are finished writing your letter to God, ask Him to help you write a letter to the abuser. Don't make plans to give it to him unless God leads you to do so. In this letter, let the abuser know that he hurt you and your loved ones but that you are prepared to forgive him and move on (not back in!). Say whatever you need to say, as long as it ends with your willingness to forgive him. This is not about denying that he hurt you; it's about freeing yourself up to move ahead with your new life and new identity. Surrender your hurt and anger to God and trust Him to avenge and restore you.

Next, write short letters to family members who were damaged due to the abusive relationship. Simply let them know how sorry you are that your relationship with the abuser caused them harm and that you are praying for their recovery and restoration. End the letters by asking them to forgive you for your part in that relationship.

It is okay to give the letters to your family members as long as you are not blaming someone else for your part or justifying your behavior or judgment calls. As long as you approach them with humility, they will more than likely be willing to forgive you. If not, ask God to help that to happen.

Last but not least, forgive God and forgive yourself. You know from the section about forgiveness how important this step is. By the time you have accomplished all of the above, your painful, ugly past should no longer have a death grip on you. Granted, it is a process, but you have made an amazing amount of progress!

# Section IX

# God Keeps Giving

---

*Although God is not* a God of methods, He is a God of order. There is no step-by-step process that applies to each and every person, but there are principles that do apply in every case. Whether your goal for reading and completing this study guide was to learn how to let go of or avoid a relationship or to recover from one, one thing applies either way: If you do not know who you are, someone else will always be willing to tell you. Unless that "someone" is God, nobody has the right or the freedom to establish your identity.

If we as women were as desperate for God as many of us are for a man, our entire lives would be more satisfying and productive. Choosing to have a personal relationship with God does not preclude you from having a personal relationship with a man. On the contrary, knowing God and yourself more intimately will only enhance your personal relationships—with all people, including those of the opposite sex!

## God Gives Protection and Safety

What does a personal relationship with God offer? First, He will protect you and keep you safe. (Psalm 27:5)

*"For in the day of trouble he will keep me safe in his dwelling; he will hide me in the shelter of his tabernacle and set me high upon a rock."* (NIV)

Having experienced abuse firsthand, you can appreciate the opportunity to be kept safely hidden from harm. Why didn't God protect you before? If you're still alive to read this, He did keep you from death. But why didn't He keep you from being abused?

The answer goes back to the issue of our free will. It wasn't God's will for you to be abused or harmed in any way. It was the will of the one with whom you chose to be in an intimate relationship. In this case, wisdom is the preventative cure. If you will trust God with your life, your relationships, and your future, He will be faithful to steer you away from someone who will exercise his free will to harm you.

God sees the big picture whereas you see only a small part. He knows the nature, character, and intentions of every living creature. While you were seeking one who would meet your needs the way you thought they needed to be met, the one you found had his own agenda—to have his own needs met. If one or both parties was looking to the other to have their needs met, the relationship was doomed from the beginning. As we say in Texas, that's like two ticks with no dog!

It is not true that each person in a couple represents one half. What we don't understand in most cases is that in order to find and maintain a relationship that will be safe, stable, and productive for a lifetime, we should not be looking for "our other half." That implies that God did not create us to be whole. That's why many women are so desperate to find the "man of their dreams." We want someone to "complete" us. And someone will. But under those circumstances and with that mindset, that "someone" will inevitably be the wrong one.

## God Gives Wholeness and Completeness

There is only one way to become whole or complete, and that is through a relationship with God Himself. (1 Thessalonians 5:23–24)

> *"May God himself, the God who makes everything holy and whole, make you holy and whole, put you together—spirit, soul, and body—and keep you fit for the coming of our Master, Jesus Christ. The One who called you is completely dependable. If he said it, he'll do it!"* (Message)

Two wounded halves never make a healthy whole. What we usually do is bundle up our baggage and drag it around until we find someone who is willing to take us "as is." That sounds noble of the other person, but he, too, has baggage and wants the same thing. When that happens, two people (usually wounded) with lots of baggage come together with the unrealistic expectation that the other will be the answer to his or her brokenness. How can one wounded soul heal another? Is that not like expecting the blind to lead the blind?

God invented modern math, and in God's mathematics, two whole people make one. That's not to say that one wounded person cannot marry another or that we have to be perfect before we get married. That's simply not going to happen. It means that two people cannot look to each other to be made complete. We have to find our completeness in Him. We can do that with a mate, if both people are willing to do so. That's why God instructs us to not be unequally yoked.

> *"Don't become partners with those who reject God. How can you make a partnership out of right and wrong? That's not partnership; that's war. Is light best friends with dark? Does Christ go strolling with the Devil? Do trust and mistrust hold hands?"* 2 Corinthians 6:14–16 (Message)

That's how abusive relationships begin. One party demands to be served. If the man with whom you choose to be intimate refuses to serve God, you can be sure he will expect you to serve him. If you are aware of this going into the relationship, you are exercising your free will, and God will not override it. You will be put in the position of trying to serve two masters: God, and a man who wants to be his own god. Matthew 6:24 says:

> *"No one can serve two masters; for either he will hate the one and love the other, or he will be devoted to one and despise the other...."* (NAS)

God will be faithful to steer you away from abusive relationships if you will commit to listen to Him.

> *"...but whoever listens to me will live in safety and be at ease, without fear of harm."* Proverbs 1:33 (NIV)

## God Gives Wisdom, Guidance, and Instruction

What else can you gain through a personal relationship with God? He will lead, guide, and instruct you as He establishes a straight path on which to walk. Because He sees the whole picture, He knows which paths lead to destruction and which people will take you down wrong paths. We can save ourselves years—or even a lifetime—of unnecessary grief and struggling if we'll trust Him in this area.

> *"I guide you in the way of wisdom and lead you along straight paths. When you walk, your steps will not be hampered; when you run, you will not stumble. Hold on to instruction, do not let it go; guard it well, for it is your life."* Proverbs 4:11 (NIV)

An intimate relationship with God is a process, just like any other relationship. As a result, we are bound to miss the mark, misunderstand, or misbehave along the way. That doesn't bother

God at all, as long as we continue wholeheartedly with the relationship. Because He knows we're going to blow it every now and then, He makes provisions for those times, even before we do it.

God is not concerned for His own sake when we make wrong choices; He just doesn't want us to lose heart in the process. Some decisions take us down paths that rob us of more than just time. A seriously wrong move can cost us our peace, health, family, job, or home.

Just like a loving parent expects of his child, God expects us to make mistakes and to fail. His desire is that we not fall down and stay down. If we fall and we're willing to get up, He will always help us. But like any loving Father, He wants to see us move full-speed ahead into the good things He has planned for us. That includes getting married and having children, if that's what we desire.

We can never have too much of God's wisdom. His wisdom not only keeps us from harm, it shows us how to prosper and grow. It is His wisdom that confirms when we are in right relationships or warns us when we are in wrong ones.

The church has come to believe a form of ungodly wisdom that says a woman must give up her own identity when she marries so that she can become "one" with her husband, who is head of the house and the relationship. In God's kingdom, both the man and the woman are to keep their God-given identities to become one in Him. What is His primary reason for the two becoming one?

> *"Has not the Lord made them one? In flesh and spirit they are his. And why one? Because he was seeking godly offspring...."* Malachi 2:15 (NIV)

God never intended for a woman to disappear into a man. If we were disposable, He wouldn't have gone to such great lengths to see that we are fearfully and wonderfully made. He wants two whole people to become one in Him so that a lineage of godly offspring can continue.

That is another case for not being unequally yoked. Even though the unbelieving husband has been sanctified through his wife (1 Corinthians 7:14), he is not likely to bring up his children in the ways of God. The children will be considered godly offspring because of the sanctified wife, but in the natural, the lives of the children may not reflect that.

Having a relationship with God is not mutually exclusive. It is not an either-or situation. If you want to be married, He wants you to be married. But He wants to give you the wisdom to discern the "right one." That doesn't mean there is just one "right one" in the entire universe. That would involve a whole lot of unnecessary stress and pressure, and that's not God's will at all. He's not playing some kind of cosmic game, and He's not out to control you or to deprive you of happiness.

Should the Lord bring that special someone into your life, it is important to surrender completely and discern accurately whether this is "the one." You are not the only one who will be affected by this relationship. The lives of your children, both born and unborn, and generations after them, will be greatly impacted by your choice of a lifelong mate. It is only wise to allow God to lead, guide, and instruct you onto a straight path. Anything short of that will put you in jeopardy of making a huge and unnecessary mistake.

## God Promises to Meet Your Needs

A personal relationship with God also ensures that your needs will be met. Luke 12:29–31 says:

> *"And do not set your heart on what you will eat or drink; do not worry about it. For the pagan world runs after all such things, and your Father knows that you need them. But seek his kingdom, and these things will be given to you as well."* (NIV)

God is saying that if you seek Him first, you won't have to worry about where your next meal is coming from or how your bills will be paid. But you can't worry a little here and there or seek only a part of His kingdom while seeking your own. You have to commit to doing it one way or the other, or you cannot expect the results God promises. It is in your best interest to commit wholeheartedly to God. You've already seen what happens when you take care of things on your own!

## God Gives You the Desires of Your Heart

Some of us have been programmed to believe that if we sell out to God, we can want only what He wants. That's not true. He has no use for a bunch of robots. A personal relationship with God comes with the promise that He'll give us the desires of our heart. Jesus says in John 15:7–8:

> "If you abide in Me, and My words abide in you, ask whatever you wish, and it will be done for you. My Father is glorified by this, that you bear much fruit, and so prove to be My disciples." (NAS)

When you shine, the Father shines. It makes Him look good. And when you make God look good, He can't help but overwhelm you with blessings. When our children brag about us, it makes us want to do even more for them. That's the way God is, and nobody can bless like He can!

## Topic for Thought

If God told you that He had the "perfect" mate for you and that you would spend the rest of your life in wedded bliss, would you trust His choice for you?

If He told you that you would have to wait five years for this "perfect" mate, would you be willing to do so?

## Exercise

You've done a lot of work up to this point and you probably need a break. For this exercise, get alone with God for an hour, if possible. Pray and tell Him how much you appreciate Him for who He is, for all He's done, and for all He's going to do in your life. Tell Him who you want to be, in Him.

As God "speaks" to you, write in your journal any insight He gives you about what He wants to do in you, for you, and through you. It may be that He longs to give you an abundance of wisdom. He may just want to spend more time with you so the two of you can have a closer walk. He might show you a picture or give you a vision. Just kick back and let Him say what He wants to say.

# Section X

# The Process of Restoration

---

*You have come an* incredibly long way in a short period of time. But you are not the person today that you will be tomorrow or the next day. That is why it is so essential to be made whole in Him before seeking a lifelong mate. The man you will attract while in a broken, vulnerable state will not be the same man you will attract when you are healed and whole, confident and prosperous.

After all the hard work you have done in this workbook, the one you will now attract is the one who will add to you, not take from you. You are now able to attract one who will love you like Christ loves the church. Ephesians 5:25–30 says:

> *"Husbands, go all out in your love for your wives, exactly as Christ did for the church—a love marked by giving, not getting. Christ's love makes the church whole. His words evoke her beauty. Everything he does and says is designed to bring the best out of her, dressing her in dazzling white silk, radiant with holiness. And that is how husbands ought also to love their own wives as their own bodies. He who loves his own wife loves himself; for no one ever hated his own flesh, but nourishes and cherishes it, just as Christ also does the church, because we are members of His body."* (Message)

If that's what God wants for His women, why should we want or settle for anything less? The "right one" will find you as you go about your Father's business, seeking His kingdom first. *Then* these things will be added to you. That's God's order, and He will honor you for obeying Him.

## Restoration Does Not Accidentally Happen

Restoration is an ongoing process, and you won't accidentally get there. You must co-labor with God to go where He wants to take you. In order to do that, you must give all power over you to Him, not to yourself or any other human. You cannot serve two masters at one time. Choose your one and only Master and go with Him alone. That means that you, and only you, are to be accountable for your thoughts, beliefs, and actions. Otherwise, the power over you belongs to someone else, and nobody other than God should ever be in that position.

There may be items in your life that represent soul ties to your abuser. These items may still bind you to your painful past. It might be jewelry, furniture, photos, videos, clothes, music, etc. In Jane's case, it was all of the above. Every item that was associated with a memory or a soul tie she disposed of or gave away. You may not be in the position to do that right away. But as God leads and enables you, be faithful to give away, sell, or throw away everything that draws you back into your past, believing that God will replace those items with new ones that speak of your new identity and your hope-filled future.

> *"Do not call to mind the former things, or ponder things of the past. Behold, I will do something new, now it will spring forth; will you not be aware of it? I will even make a road-way in the wilderness, rivers in the desert."* Isaiah 43:18–19 (NAS)

## God Restores Valuable Relationships

God not only wants to restore *you*, He is a restorer of valuable, life-giving relationships as well. As part of the abuse, you probably became secluded from friends and family and other people who were important to you. It's time to reclaim those relationships and to forge new ones. God is all about relationships. That's one way He reveals Himself; He works through people to bless and encourage us, to help us, and to grow and develop us in ways we could never accomplish on our own.

This is no time to be the Lone Ranger. Don't try to heal and recover on your own. You have renounced shame, embarrassment, guilt, and unworthiness. It's time to start owning your right to love and be loved. Trust God to connect you with the right people for this season of your life. And don't expect always to be the one who is blessed; purpose to bless others as well. You are worthy to do that! The important thing is to connect with others.

> *"By yourself you're unprotected. With a friend you can face the worst. Can you round up a third? A three-stranded rope isn't easily snapped."* Ecclesiastes 4:12 (Message)

## God Gives New Ways of Thinking

God wants to replace all your old habits and ways of thinking. You must break ties with people and places that help to perpetuate your old, destructive ways. If you found comfort in a relationship that focused on what was wrong in your life, either change the nature of the relationship or move on. If you can help pull that friend, relative, or co-worker out of the ditch, then by all means, do so. But if he or she is not ready for a new life and still prefers the old, shake the dust off your feet and move on.

> *"Your old life is dead. Your new life, which is your real life— even though invisible to spectators—is with Christ in God. He is your life. When Christ (your real life, remember) shows*

*up again on this earth, you'll show up, too—the real you, the glorious you. Meanwhile, be content with obscurity, like Christ. And that means killing off everything connected with that way of death: sexual promiscuity, impurity, lust, doing whatever you feel like whenever you feel like it, and grabbing whatever attracts your fancy. That's a life shaped by things and feelings instead of by God…."* Colossians 3:5 (Message)

## God Will Soften Your Heart

God also wants to restore your vulnerability. A hardened heart can neither bless nor receive. Be transparent. You don't have to offer up your business to strangers and to people who do not have your best interests at heart. But be open and honest with your true friends and confidantes. Level with them about your struggles. Be accountable. Ask them to pray for you; they'll help keep you straight.

*"Do not lie to each other, since you have taken off your old self with its practices and have put on the new self, which is being renewed in knowledge in the image of its Creator."* Colossians 3:9 (NIV)

## God Restores Finances

God wants to restore your finances as well. Maybe you were never taught how to manage finances, or maybe you never had the freedom to earn, spend, and save money. Today is a new day, and the old days are dead and gone. 2 Corinthians 5:17 says:

*"Now we look inside, and what we see is that anyone united with the Messiah gets a fresh start, is created new. The old life is gone; a new life burgeons!"* (Message)

Do not be intimidated by the prospect of managing finances. Trust God to lead, guide, and instruct you, and He will see that all your needs are met. Remember to first seek His kingdom; when you are faithful to take care of His business, He'll be pleased and faithful to take care of yours.

Three other essential ingredients in the recipe of financial prosperity include integrity and tithing and giving.

Financial integrity is not optional. God takes integrity seriously; if we are wheeling and dealing in His name, it better be an accurate reflection of who He is.

> *"God hates cheating in the marketplace; he loves it when business is aboveboard."* Proverbs 11:1 (Message)

> *"Wealth obtained by fraud dwindles, but the one who gathers by labor increases it."* Proverbs 13:11 (NAS)

> *"If you're honest in small things, you'll be honest in big things; If you're a crook in small things, you'll be a crook in big things. If you're not honest in small jobs, who will put you in charge of the store?"* Luke 16:10–12 (Message)

Giving is a biblical principle. You may not be familiar with the concept of tithing; however, you need not only to be aware, but to obey. Just like financial integrity, tithing and giving are not optional. If you refuse to tithe, your finances are under a curse.

In the world's economy, we are taught that in order to survive, we must scrimp and save and stash enough money for old age and to get through a crisis. There is nothing wrong with saving and being prepared. But the way to prosper financially is not to hoard your money. That shows a lack of faith in God that He will, in fact, provide for all your needs. Because God gives freely, we need to give freely. We must commit to represent Him well at all times.

> *"Sinners are always wanting what they don't have; the God-loyal are always giving what they do have."* Proverbs 21:26 (Message)

Remember that all good gifts come from God. If you have a job, thank Him; He provided it for you. All He asks in return is one-tenth of what He gives you. That leaves you with ninety percent! God doesn't need your money. He needs your trust and obedience so He can bless you without ceasing.

> *"Will a man rob God? Yet you are robbing Me! But you say, 'How have we robbed You?' In tithes and offerings. You are cursed with a curse, for you are robbing Me, the whole nation of you! Bring the whole tithe into the storehouse, so that there may be food in My house, and test Me now in this,"* says the Lord of hosts, *"if I will not open for you the windows of heaven and pour out for you a blessing until it overflows. Then I will rebuke the devourer for you, so that it will not destroy the fruits of the ground; nor will your vine in the field cast its grapes,"* says the Lord of hosts. *"All the nations will call you blessed, for you shall be a delightful land,"* says the Lord of hosts.* Malachi 3:8–12 (NAS)

One of the best possible ways to break free of the victim mentality is to meet one of God's challenges. If He challenges you to do something, it's because He wants to promote and bless you beyond your wildest dreams. He warns us about cursing our own finances by not giving tithes and offerings. Then He instructs us to test Him by obeying so He can bless us mightily for all to see. He wants to make us examples of His goodness, and that means you!

## God Restores Dreams

God also wants to restore your dreams and the desires of your heart. Who did you want to be before you got shot down? Jane wanted to be an attorney or a detective when she was growing up. When that idea got blown out of the water, she wanted to become a doctor or a nurse. God put those desires in her heart. She first wanted to be in the position to seek justice for those who could not help themselves. She then wanted to heal and nurture the wounded and injured.

Can you guess what Jane is doing now? She has established a nonprofit organization called Jane's House Ministries so she can lead wounded and injured women to restoration, healing, and a new identity in Jesus Christ. God remembered the desires of Jane's heart when she was young. Now, decades and many mistakes later, He is honoring them as if nothing had ever deterred her. Jane's lack of formal education was not an obstacle for God. Her willingness to trust and obey Him was the only ticket she needed.

> *"What then shall we say to these things? If God is for us, who is against us?"* Romans 8:31 (NAS)

> *"…Jesus said, 'With people it is impossible, but not with God; for all things are possible with God.'"* Mark 10: 27 (NAS)

## Exercise

Now that you are armed with forgiveness, a clean slate, and the power of God, say a final goodbye to your past and move full-speed ahead with your new identity and new future. Write in your journal the changes God has made in you and for you from the time you began reading *Me Man, You Woman: Jane's Deliverance from an Abusive Marriage*, until now, since you've completed the study guide. Commit to give Him thanks, honor, and praise every single day. Gratitude is a key to continued blessings.

The final part of this exercise is to love God, yourself, and others and to become the person you wanted to be before you got shot down.

You can congratulate yourself and enjoy your wonderful accomplishment! Thank you for your hard work in following through with these exercises and for giving yourself a chance to be healed and restored. May God bless you, keep you, and prosper you all the days of your life.

# Breaking Free Journal

Sponsored by Jane's House Ministries

Where Healing and Restoration Begin

# Section 1

---

## The Generational Cycle

# Section II

## Knowing the Truth Will Set You Free

*"That if you confess with your mouth, 'Jesus is Lord,' and believe in your heart that God raised him from the dead, you will be saved. For it is with your heart that you believe and are justified, and it is with your mouth that you confess and are saved."* Romans 10:9–10 (NIV)

*"This is how much God loved [          ]: He gave his Son, his one and only Son. And this is why: so that [          ] need not be destroyed; by believing in him, [          ] can have a whole and lasting life. God didn't go to all the trouble of sending his Son merely to point an accusing finger at [          ], telling her how bad she was.* He came to help her, to put her right again. Because she trusts in him, [          ] is acquitted." John 3:16–18 [Emphasis mine]

*"Praise the Lord, O my soul, and forget not all his benefits—who forgives all your sins and heals all your diseases,* who redeems your life from the pit and crowns you with love and compassion, *who satisfies your desires with good things so that your youth is renewed like the eagle's."* Psalm 103:2–5 (NIV) [Emphasis mine]

*"God makes everything come out right; he puts victims back on their feet."* Psalm 103:6 (Message)

*"I know what I'm doing. I have it all planned out—plans to take care of you, not abandon you. Plans to give you the future you hope for."* Jeremiah 29:11 (Message)

*"...and you will know the truth, and the truth will make you free."* John 8:32 (Message)

_____

_____

_____

_____

_____

_____

_____

_____

_____

_____

_____

_____

_____

_____

_____

_____

_____

_____

_____

_____

_____

# Section III

God Knows You Well

_____

_____

_____

_____

_____

_____

_____

_____

_____

_____

_____

_____

_____

_____

_____

_____

_____

_____

# Section IV

---

## The Power of Agreement

# Section V

## Understanding the Cycle of Abuse

_____

_____

_____

_____

_____

_____

_____

_____

_____

_____

_____

_____

_____

_____

_____

_____

_____

_____

_____
_____
_____
_____
_____
_____
_____
_____
_____
_____
_____
_____
_____
_____
_____
_____
_____
_____
_____
_____
_____
_____
_____
_____

_____

_____

_____

_____

_____

_____

_____

_____

_____

_____

_____

_____

_____

_____

_____

_____

_____

_____

_____

_____

_____

_____

_____

_____

_____

_____

_____

_____

_____

_____

_____

_____

_____

_____

_____

_____

_____

_____

_____

_____

_____

_____

_____

# Section VI

## The Power of Forgiveness

_____

_____

_____

_____

_____

_____

_____

_____

_____

_____

_____

_____

_____

_____

# Section VII

---

## Discover Your God-Designed Identity

*There is nothing I don't know about you.* (Psalm 139:1)

*I made you in My image.* (Genesis 1:27)

*You are My child.* (Acts 17:28)

*I knew you before you were conceived; you were My idea.* (Jeremiah 1:5)

*I chose you when I planned creation.* (Ephesians 1:11)

*Nothing about you is a mistake; I carefully crafted every part of you.* (Psalm 139:15)

*I know what you're going to do each day; your days are recorded in My book.* (Psalm 139:16)

*I decided exactly when you would be born and where you would live.* (Acts 17:26)

*I know exactly how you were made; I crafted you Myself.* (Psalm 139:14)

*I decided every last detail about you—inside and out—from the time you were conceived.* (Psalm 139:13)

*When you were fully formed, I called you forth from your mother's womb.* (Psalm 71:6)

*I am not distant and angry; I am the perfect and complete expression of love.* (1 John 4:16)

*I long to consume you with My love because you are My child and I am your Father.* (1 John 3:1)

*Your earthly father cannot come close to giving you what I can.* (Matthew 7:11)

*I am the perfect Father in every way.* (Matthew 5:48)

*Every time you receive a good gift, know it's from Me.* (James 1:17)

*Don't worry about how you will survive; I know all your needs. Look to Me first and I will take care of you.* (Matthew 6:31–33)

*Choose My plan for your future; it is full of hope.* (Jeremiah 29:11)

*I have never quit loving you and I never will.* (Jeremiah 31:3)

*My thoughts of you outnumber the grains of sand on the seashore; you are always on My mind!* (139:17–18)

*I celebrate you by singing over you.* (Zephaniah 3:17)

*My mind is made; I will never stop doing good to you.* (Jeremiah 32:40)

*You are My special treasure.* (Exodus 19:5)

*I will stick with you no matter what; I will be so good to you, you won't even consider turning away from Me.* (Jeremiah 32:41)

*I'll tell you marvelous and wondrous things that you could never figure out on your own.* (Jeremiah 33:3)

*If you seek Me with everything you have, you will find Me.* (Deuteronomy 4:29)

*Delight yourself in Me and I will give you your heart's desires.* (Psalm 37:4)

*For it is I who gave you those desires.* (Philippians 2:13)

*On your best day, you cannot imagine all that I can do for you!* (Ephesians 3:20)

*I am your greatest fan and will never stop helping and encouraging you.* (2 Thessalonians 2:16–17)

*When you are having trouble, look for Me; I will be there to comfort you.* (2 Corinthians 1:3–4)

*When you are brokenhearted, I am right next to you.* (Psalm 34:18)

*Like a good shepherd carries a lamb, I have carried you next to My heart.* (Isaiah 40:11)

*One day, I will wipe away all of your tears and you will no longer cry, be sad, or feel pain.* (Revelation 21:3–4)

*I am your Father and I love you in the same way I love My Son, Jesus.* (John 17:23)

*I am on your side; you cannot lose!* (Romans 8:31)

*I'm not keeping track of your sins and mistakes.* (2 Corinthians 5:19)

*Through Me, you can conquer any and every thing that opposes you.* (Romans 8:37)

_____

_____

_____

_____

_____

_____

_____

# Section VIII

Own Your Actions and Decisions

# Section IX

## God Keeps Giving

_____

_____

_____

_____

_____

_____

_____

_____

_____

_____

_____

_____

_____

_____

_____

_____

_____

# Section X

## The Process of Restoration

# The Authors

---

**Rhonda Tarver** is co-founder and editor-in-chief of Our Destiny Publishing, LLC. She has nearly twenty-five years of experience in the publishing and communications fields and is a member of such organizations as the International Women's Writing Guild and the National Writers Association. She has experience ghostwriting for four weekly syndicated newspapers, has been a regular contributor of technical articles for communications publications, and has written a series of personal testimonies of people whose lives have been transformed by the power of God. She and her daughter Lyndsay have earned black belts in kickboxing. Now a doting grandmother to Anthony, Rhonda resides in Stafford, Texas, where she is a member of Abiding Life Christian Fellowship.

**Trudy Michalak** is the founder of Jane's House Ministries, a non-profit dedicated to helping women recover from abusive relationships. A native of Cleveland, Ohio, she and her now-deceased husband, David, moved in 1980 to the Houston area, where their three daughters were born. Trudy now works with friends and partners Rhonda Tarver and Danny Lee to advance their recently-established publishing company, Our Destiny Publishing, LLC. Trudy, who attends Abiding Life Christian Fellowship in Stafford, Texas, enjoys watching old movies, listening to classic rock music, singing, and praise-and-worship dancing. Her mission in life is to spread the good news of God's love for women and His plans to restore broken lives.

## Give the Gift of

# Breaking Free
## from the Victim Mentality

### A Study Guide/Personal Journal for
## *Me Man, You Woman*
*Jane's Deliverance from an Abusive Marriage*

## to Your Friends and Colleagues

### CHECK YOUR LEADING BOOKSTORE OR ORDER HERE

❑ **YES**, I want _____ copies of ***Me Man, You Woman***: *Jane's Deliverance from an Abusive Marriage* at $15.95 each, plus $3.95 shipping per book (Texas residents please add $1.32 sales tax per book).

❑ **YES**, I want _____ copies of ***Breaking Free from the Victim Mentality*** at $13.95 each, plus $2.95 shipping per book (Texas residents please add $1.15 sales tax per book).

**Canadian orders must be accompanied by a postal money order in U.S. funds. Allow 15 days for delivery.**

❑ **YES**, I am interested in having the author speak or give a seminar to my company, association, school, or organization. Please send information.

My check or money order for $_____ is enclosed.

Please charge my:    ❑ Visa      ❑ MasterCard
                        ❑ Discover    ❑ American Express

Name _____

Organization _____

Address _____

City/State/Zip _____

Phone_____ Email _____

Card # _____

Exp. Date_____ Signature _____

*Please make your check payable and return to:* Our Destiny Publishing, LLC
5680 Highway 6 South #390 • Missouri City, TX 77459

**Call your credit card order to: (281) 933-4990 or (866) 933-4990**
Fax: (832) 201-8635        **www.ourdestinypublishing.com**